Dianaisms

by

Dr. Diana D. Light

Art by
Jake Shandy
JakeShandy.com

ISBN: 978-1-931895-04-0

PROLOGUE

What is a "Dianaism?"

It is a very short thought, like an AH-**HA**, that just comes to you seemingly out of Nowhere, which makes a lot of sense at the time.

Is Diana the only one who can write these?

No. Anyone can receive these Shards of Light in the form of Insightful Words.

How do I make them mine?

All you need to do when you receive an "Ism" is to write it down quickly, before it disappears.

Is that all?

No. Now for the best part. You can make them yours. Just put "YourFirstName" in front of the "ism" and you will have written and claimed your Own "isms!"

How do I start?

When you read this Book, you'll get the idea. At the end of the Book are some blank pages for you to write down your very own "isms." Then you can share them with others and show them how.

You could even have An "Ism" Party
And Everyone can play!

I Long To Be

A Painter

Of

Words

Thus

It Befits

Quips

From

My Lips

Drips

One Feather

Does not

A

Bird

Make

Sing

Every day

And no clouds

Will come your

way!

As I breathe in Love...
My eyes twinkle Light
Sparkle, Sparkle

As I breathe out Love
I see you more clearly...

Longing
Shifts Presence
Into
An Abyss
Unaware…

Where stillness
is left
Far Behind

My Essence cannot come or go

It cannot fight

It cannot work for it.

It just IS...

Organized

Energy

Manifests
Form

Whatever You Think as
Your Reality…
No matter how thwarted
Or accurate…
It Becomes
Who
You Are

All I have to do is

Match my Actions with

My Feeling...

AND BE LOVE...

When I Enjoy Good
I Ignore Bad

I'm Too Busy Adding
To My Life
To Let Anything Or
Anybody Take Away
From My Life

Spaces Around Stacks

Makes Stacks

Seem Smaller

Collected Clutter

Looks Better

Than

Dispersed Clutter

Therefore

"Keep It Together"

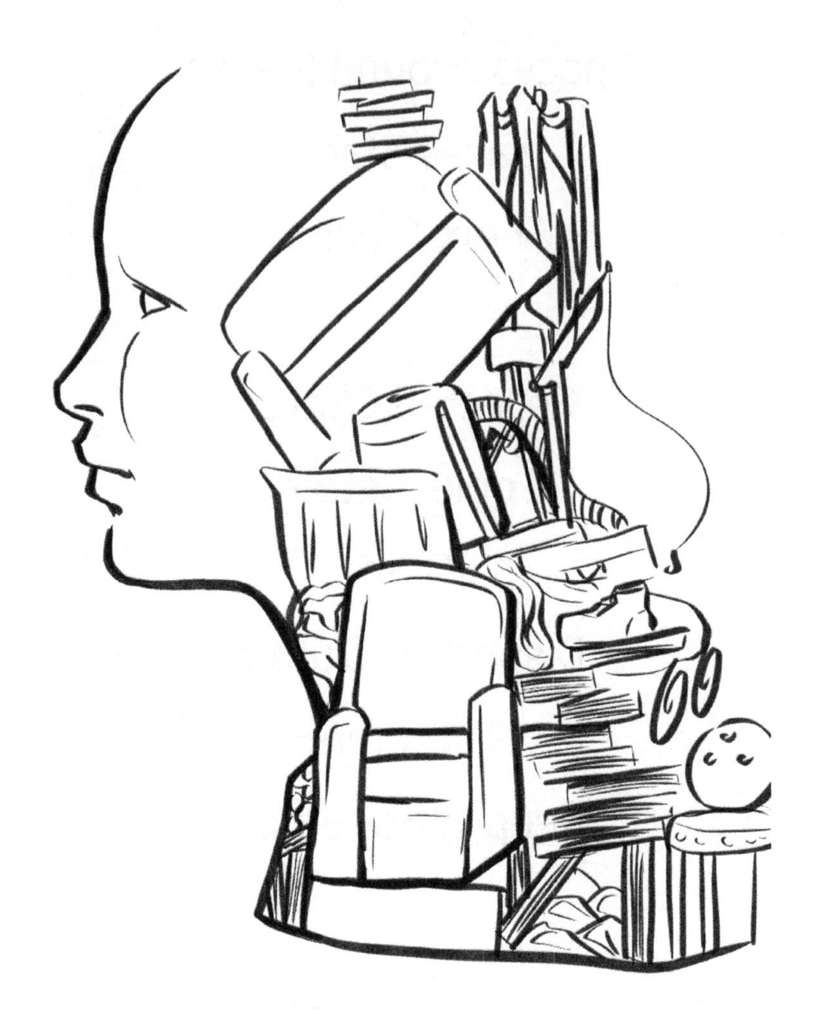

A Goal Set

Is not...

A Goal Met

Yet.

Impossible Paradox
Journey of Becoming
What I Already Am

Acceptance Begets Love

Women cannot make
Men think like Women…

Women can Love men into
Who they really are…

By Loving themselves and
Sharing their Wisdom.

Act as if...
and
You are...

All you got to do is "Feel Good"
And "Do Good"

Tickle Your Imagination

Be As **Big** As You

Can **Be**

The Difference Between
Husband and Wife

The Husband makes a Living
For the Home

The Wife makes the Home
Worth Living in.

I shine
with the Luminosity
of a Billion Stars

As I loosen my fetters,
and move in the direction
of the Song of my Soul...

The path
clearly
appears...

AWAKE

See

Feel

Hear

Smell

Taste

Listen

to

Everything

NEW

Be the
You
You
Wanna Be

He who carries Black Cloud

Over Head

Is shaded from

De – Light

The problem with you is

You don't think

Big enough...

The problem with me is

The bigger I think

The bigger I think

I am...

I get to Change

History by Loving

Me in the Present!

Divine
Flow
is

The
Loving
Way to Go

Silence is the

Unexpressed

Potential

Of All Sound

If I didn't know
"I don't know how..."

What I would do is...

Solve
the
Problem...

Plan for the Une pected

x

You just don't know
What you don't know

Until you do.

Drain
Brain
Strain

I never met a
Person I didn't
Like...

Some are more
Like me than others...

Dumb Things

Do

Happen to

Smart

People

Hunter says I am
Ephemeral…

Who Do I say I am?

Everywhere
I Look

I see
Something
New and Exciting

Love is a Gift

To Add up
Subtract yourself

I joyously e x p a n d into
More Love
Passion and Joy
In Abundance...easily now

A n d I d e s e r v e i t.

That Which I Want...

I Give...

Feelings move quickly
Without Thoughts...

A Kiss

Like Bliss

Is

Spoiled by

A

Miss

Flip It

FLIP IT!!

When the Truth of the
Moment
Meets at the Epicenter of
the Paradox
The Mind goes Silent
The Heart feels Truth
And the Soul goes Free

Give Away Something
Every Day!
And
Watch your smile
Grow…

I Am Good Enough to
Get Out Of Anything...

Even When I Am Not
Smart Enough to
Know How
To Not Get In...

Ground Is Where You Go To Take Off Again Isn't It?

I Think I Could Be Happier

If I Poured More Of Me

Into The Reality Of Now--

And Quit Building My

Nows Around Nevers.

YOU CAN HAVE

SUCCESS

WHILE BECOMING

SUCCESSFUL!!!

You ARE who you SAY you ARE...

I am having trouble
Liking where you are,

'Cause I know
Where you are not!

I am Not
Touchable
by
What
Isn't
Real...

Precious
Are the Moments
from
Birth to Birth…

Eternal
and
Ever Lasting…

I Am Relaxed
in the
Flowing Pleasure
of Life bringing
Love into Loving easily...

My Wheels Are Spinning

My Motor Is Racing

But My Car In On A Jack

Since Nothing Is Touching

The Ground

What do I do about that?

I Am Not More Than Nor Am I Less Than

I Gave Up My Need

To Know...

A Stone is rolled from the

Tomb of my Longing...

And I am Free to Be

Who I choose to Be...

Name It

Name It!

Claim It!

State What You want...
State When You want it...

Start Attracting
It to You...

The Universe will supply
The "How" it comes
And "Who" will help you

Closeness comes

From letting loose

Not from hanging on

To the Goose

The Goose will fatten

Not in hand

But reward the feeder

Oh, how grand!

I get to change

History by Loving me

In the Present.

I Trust In What

I Don't Know

And Live

What I Know...

I Will Know

What

I Need To Know

When

I Need To Know It...

If I could accept

My goofs and shortcomings

Without so much contempt...

Perhaps

I could accept You

JUST THE WAY YOU ARE...

Love is the Light

that

Dissolves all walls…

If I didn't feel stuck
What I'd do is...

Whatever
I need
to move
forward...

If You're

"Gonna"

"Get To It..."

Might as

Well

Just

"Do" it!!

To bring about complete
Outer Change

Inner change
Comes 1st

It works from...Inside Out...

Let Not...
The Little
Interferes

Pull You into
Littleness...

It's Hard To Love Someone

As Critical As I Am

Of Myself…

H - OLDING The

U - NDERSTANDING Of

G - OODNESS

It is time
to develop Serenity
Receptivity
Quiet and Joy in
"Not Knowing"

It Takes A

Level Head

To Come Out Even

Life is just like

A Bed

We're all in it

For the thrill

Of the Bounces!

Ever feel like the
Bumper in Bumper Pool?

People Bump off you
On the way to
someone
Else...

Listen

Until

Your Sounds Fill
And Overflow from Within You

then

You will Rock Their World...

There are plenty of Fish in the Sea

Some are even more intelligent,

Better educated, kinder, richer

and more Loving

Than thee

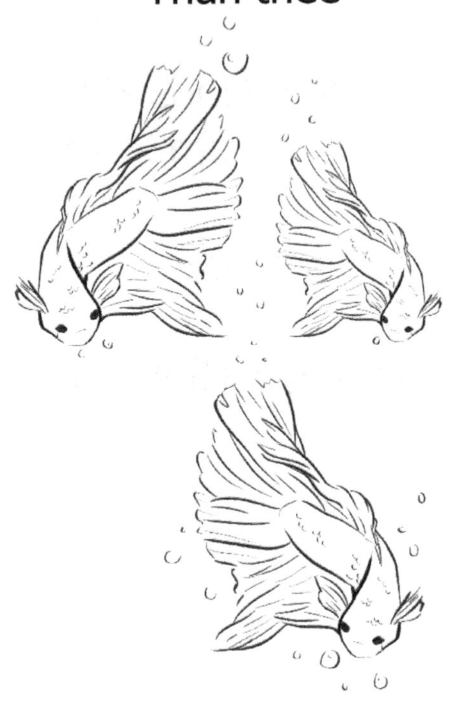

I
Am
Love
In
Process

As I
Progress
As
Love

Love is
Letting go of
Expectation…

And receiving
What's there…

Love
is
Loving
Someone
When
They don't
Feel
Lovable!

Awareness flashes
Frozen Time Conglomerates
As I Splash into Before...

Mirror Appreciation Everywhere

“As I lift my
Ceiling of Pleasure
I Watch
My Fears
All fall away.”

Laugh

Until It

Helps!

SUCCESSES do WHAT

FAILURES DON'T WANT to DO

AND THEN SOME...

There are no Goodbyes

Only

Continued Nows...

No One Is Going To Give Me

The State Of Being

(LOVE, PEACE, POWER, JOY)

I Want In My LIFE...

I MUST DO THAT!

I no longer have to try
I no longer have to...
I no longer...

I no
    I know
        I know...

There Is Nothing
To
Understand...

...Experience
The
Experience...

Now…
is the
Only Time
I Breathe
My Being into My Future…
as
I
Emerge
Stronger from
My Past

If I Don't
Choose Differently
Than I Have In The Past...

I Will Always Create
The Same Now.

Drink in the Purity You Are

Now I walk in Beauty
Beauty is before me
Beauty is behind me
Above and below me

Perhaps our greatest fear
is not that we won't be Loved
but that we will be Loved...

If we are truly Loved...
And begin to believe it
Then we'd have to give up our
belief in not being Lovable.

Then who would we Be....

One

Giant

Ball of

GO...

Flaccidity Brings
Felicity

as

Relaxation Brings
Joy!

PACE, PACE, PACE

It does not matter

If one wins the Race

What matters is the PACE…

…And the Company

I am pedaling as fast as I can

Trying to be still...

CAUTION

Personality under
Reconstruction

Wear HARD HAT

(and use Soft Heart)

Prayers are the

Invisible

Clouds of Love

That connect, inspire and

Strengthen us all.

Getting "Old" is saying
more

"No's" than before

Staying "Young" is saying
"Yes!" "Yes!" "Yes!" as
Much as possible.

Problems are what people create
so they have something to do.

What age is a
Queenager?

Any age she wants
…Eternal Youth…
is Ageless

Secret

To find Love

Let go of
Everything
That isn't

Love will then
Find you…

If you always do

What you've always done

You'll always get

What you always got

SUCCESS is in direct

PROPORTION to ONE'S

ABILITY to SEE

B E Y O N D...The PROBLEM

Tears are a...

Surrender of emotions

So that the Soul

Can remember the

Journey is

Love...

The Center Never Goes Away...

A Gift To A Boy

Could be

A Toy

Ahoy!

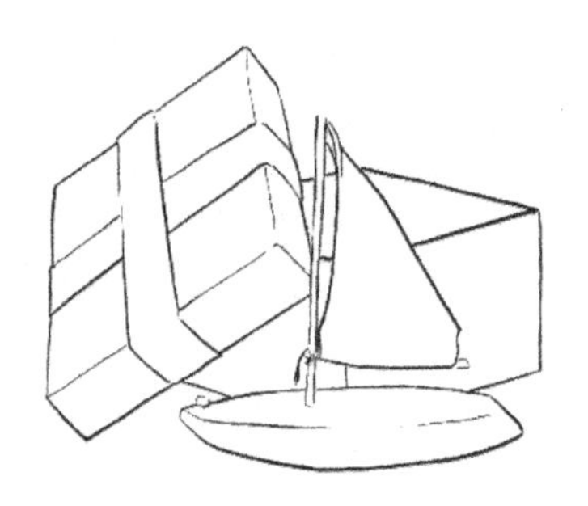

I am never late
I am never early

My Heart beats
To Divine Time

Precisely on Time
To No Time at all...

The Divine Light deep
within me
Proceeds me and shines
before me
Creating my path
Ever protecting me
Guiding me
On the Adventures
My Soul longs to take.

There are plenty of Fish in the Sea

Some are even more intelligent,

Better educated, kinder, richer

and more Loving

Than thee

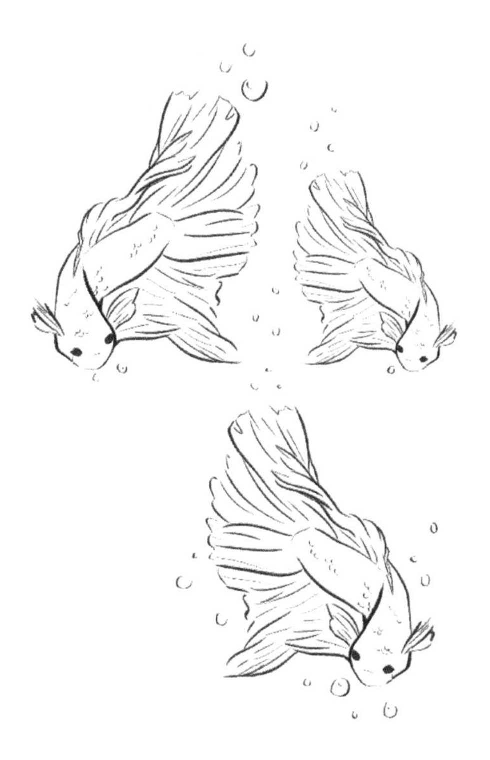

The More I Receive,

The More I Enter

The Circle Of Life
And Allow It To Flow

Easily

The Secret to
Living a Long
Life
is
To Love the Life
You Live…

Be the You You Wanna Be

There Is Nothing Missing
Love Awakens Love

There's

Sumthin

Good

About Getting

UP ^

To bring about complete

Outer Change

Inner change

Comes 1st

It works from…Inside Out…

Truth a holic

"Everyone is entitled to my Opinion"

Two Lights
Burning as One Flame
Flicker
Wherever we go...

Wishing

Put into Doing

...Brings Results...

You Attract
Who You Are!

YOU BECOME

AS YOU THINK

YOU ARE,

SO YOU BECOME…

So what're you thinking?

He who carries Black Cloud

Over Head

Is shaded from

De - Light

"You cannot be

Where

I am not going to show up"

My Ostrich Nature
Snares

Squeaky Wheels

Get greased

Quiet Wheels

Get Wear and Tear

Conclusion

Whatever I Am Feeling
Will Change...

Made in the USA
Middletown, DE
28 May 2022

66296464R00076